S0-AQL-055

My Bible Friends

To

Brian and Bruce
Randy and Diana

And

all the boys and girls
who like Bible stories

Copyright © 1963 and 1977 by
Review and Herald® Publishing Association
All Rights Are Reserved

No part of the literary or pictorial contents of
this book may be reproduced in any manner whatsoever
without written permission from the publisher.

Published jointly by
REVIEW AND HERALD® PUBLISHING ASSOCIATION
Hagerstown, MD 21740

PACIFIC PRESS PUBLISHING ASSOCIATION
Boise, ID 83707

ISBN 978-0-8280-1018-4

Library of Congress Catalog Card No. 76-55834

PRINTED IN U.S.A.

My Bible Friends

Etta B. Degering/Book Five

Illustrated by Robert Berran

The stories in this book are—

Daniel and His Friends   Zacchaeus the Cheater

Daniel and the Lions   Jabel the Shepherd

Daniel and His Friends
(Daniel 1)

It was noontime in the city of Jerusalem;
  the Temple school for boys had been dismissed.
Daniel and his three special friends
  were hurrying home to lunch,
  when suddenly a trumpet sounded!
"Ta-ee, ta-ee, ta-ee!" shrilled the trumpet.

It was the noontime call to prayer.
Three times a day—morning, noon, and night—
    a priest came out on the Temple porch
    and blew on a ram's-horn trumpet.
    "Ta-ee, ta-ee, ta-ee! It's time for prayers."
Daniel turned about-face toward the Temple.
His friends turned about-face toward the Temple.
All the people of Jerusalem stopped whatever
    they were doing and faced toward the Temple.
With heads bowed, they prayed to the God of heaven.

At home, Daniel's mother served pulse for lunch.
Pulse is food like beans and vegetables,
    brown bread, berries, and dates.
Daniel liked pulse:
    pulse would make him grow tall;
    pulse would make him grow strong;
    pulse would make him get good grades in school.

Daniel, his three friends, and all the people
    of Jerusalem felt safe in their city.
For hadn't the city a high stone wall around it?
And were there not strong gates in the wall,
    with a watchtower above each gate,
    where watchmen kept watch day and night?
If Daniel listened he would hear the watchman call,
    "First watch, all is well!" . . . and later,
    "Second watch, all is well!" . . . and still later,
    "Third watch, all is well!" . . .

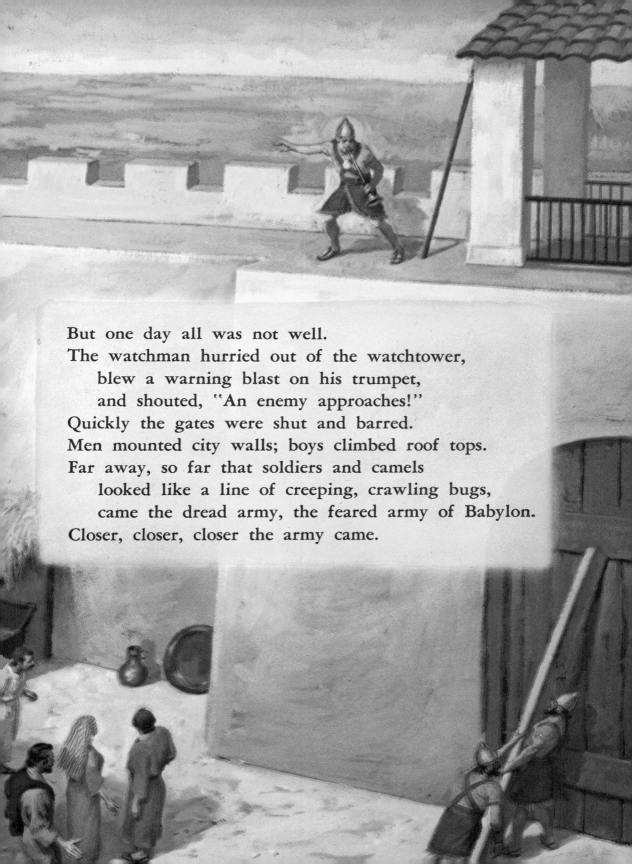

But one day all was not well.
The watchman hurried out of the watchtower,
    blew a warning blast on his trumpet,
    and shouted, "An enemy approaches!"
Quickly the gates were shut and barred.
Men mounted city walls; boys climbed roof tops.
Far away, so far that soldiers and camels
    looked like a line of creeping, crawling bugs,
    came the dread army, the feared army of Babylon.
Closer, closer, closer the army came.

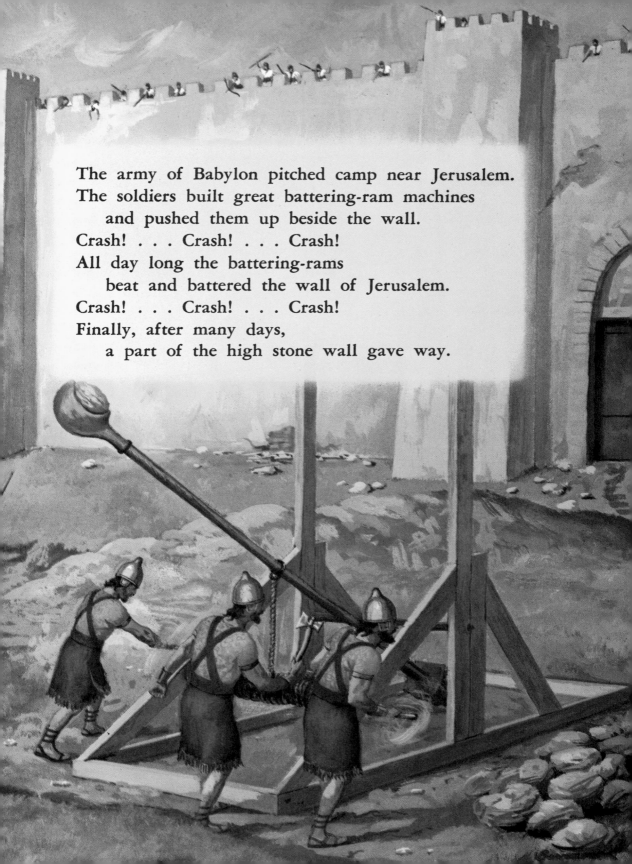

The army of Babylon pitched camp near Jerusalem.
The soldiers built great battering-ram machines
    and pushed them up beside the wall.
Crash! . . . Crash! . . . Crash!
All day long the battering-rams
    beat and battered the wall of Jerusalem.
Crash! . . . Crash! . . . Crash!
Finally, after many days,
    a part of the high stone wall gave way.

The army of Babylon marched into Jerusalem.
Some of the soldiers climbed the hill to the Temple
    and took away the Temple's golden vessels,
    as the king of Babylon had commanded them to do.
Some soldiers stood guard while
    other soldiers took men and boys prisoners.
They took Daniel and his three friends.

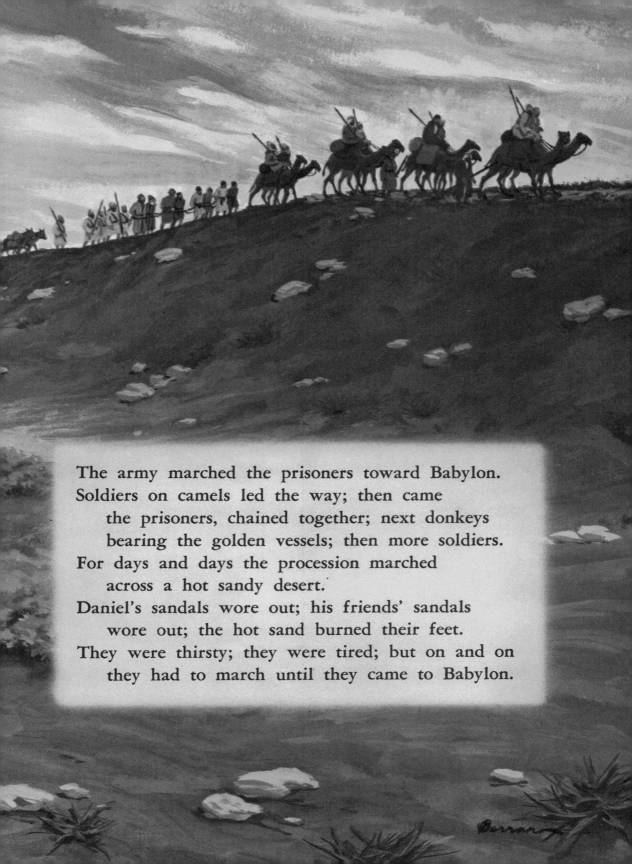

The army marched the prisoners toward Babylon.
Soldiers on camels led the way; then came
    the prisoners, chained together; next donkeys
    bearing the golden vessels; then more soldiers.
For days and days the procession marched
    across a hot sandy desert.
Daniel's sandals wore out; his friends' sandals
    wore out; the hot sand burned their feet.
They were thirsty; they were tired; but on and on
    they had to march until they came to Babylon.

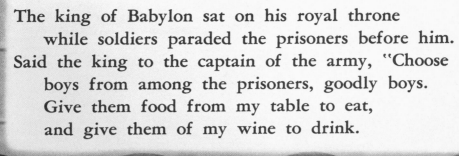

The king of Babylon sat on his royal throne
while soldiers paraded the prisoners before him.
Said the king to the captain of the army, "Choose
boys from among the prisoners, goodly boys.
Give them food from my table to eat,
and give them of my wine to drink.

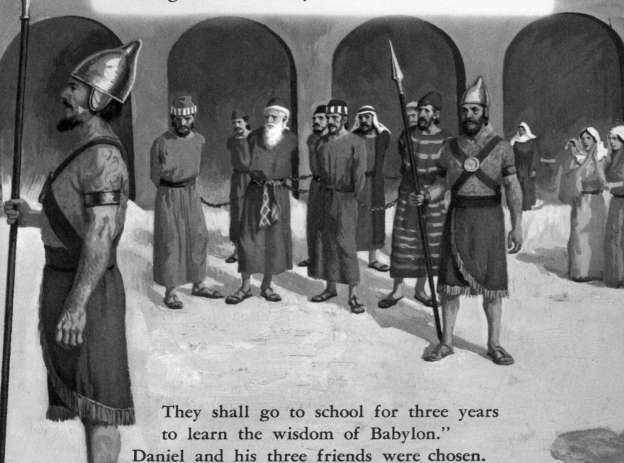

They shall go to school for three years
to learn the wisdom of Babylon."
Daniel and his three friends were chosen.
Prince Melzar was given charge over all the boys.

That evening Daniel and his friends talked together.
"We cannot eat the king's food," said Daniel.
"It has been offered to idols, and besides,
    the king's food is not the best food for boys;
    neither can we drink the king's wine."
"What shall we do?" the boys asked one another.
Then Daniel thought of a plan. "Let's ask Melzar
    to give us pulse to eat and water to drink
    instead of the king's food and wine."
"It's a good plan," agreed the three friends.

Daniel and his friends went to see Prince Melzar.
They bowed politely, then asked for pulse and water
   instead of the king's food and wine.
Melzar shook his head *NO*. "If the king should see
   you looking thinner than the other boys, and
   learn that I had given you pulse and water,
   he might—he might even cut off my head."
"Please try us for ten days," begged Daniel.
So Melzar agreed to give them pulse and water
   for ten days. "Then we shall see," he said.

Although Daniel and his friends were far from home,
and there was no sound of a ram's-horn trumpet
to remind them, they did not forget to pray.
Morning, noon, and night Daniel opened his window
toward the Temple back in Jerusalem,
and prayed to the God of heaven.
He asked God to bless the pulse and water, and
to please let it make them strong,
so that Melzar might know that pulse and water
were better for boys than the king's food and wine.

When the ten days had passed,
    Prince Melzar called all the boys before him.
He looked at their faces; he felt their arms.
He found that Daniel and his friends were
    fairer and fatter than the boys who
    ate the king's food and drank the king's wine.
So, ever after, during the three years of school,
    Prince Melzar gave Daniel and his friends
    pulse to eat and water to drink.

One . . . two . . . three years went by;
    school was over for Daniel and his friends.
They had grown taller. Had they grown wiser?
The king himself would test them.

Daniel and his friends—dressed in clean clothes,
   with hair combed, and sandals polished—
   stood before the king of Babylon.
The king asked them question after question.
And lo! The king found Daniel and his three friends
   T-E-N times wiser than all the wise men of Babylon.

Daniel and the Lions
(Daniel 6)

Many years had gone by since Daniel
    had been taken a prisoner to Babylon.
He had grown to be a wise, good man.
And now a new king sat upon the royal throne.
The new king soon learned that no matter what
    happened, he could trust Daniel.
So the new king made Daniel ruler next to himself:
    over all the people of the kingdom,
    over all the wise men of the kingdom,
    over all the princes of the kingdom.

Berran

The princes became angry when the king
    made Daniel ruler over them, so angry they
    began plotting a way to get rid of Daniel.
Said a sly prince, "We'll find some fault in him
    and go tell the king." So the princes watched
    Daniel, but not a fault could they find in him.
Daniel didn't lie; he didn't cheat;
    he was never late; he did his work well.
"I know what we can do," said the sly prince.
"Tell us," chorused the princes. "What can we do?"

"Have you not seen Daniel open his window toward
    Jerusalem, morning, noon, and night? Have you
    not heard him pray to the God of heaven?" asked
    the sly prince. "Well, we'll write a law that
    anyone who prays to any god except the king for
    thirty days shall be thrown into the lions' den."
"The king will be so pleased," said a prince,
    "he'll not think of Daniel; he'll seal the law."
"Ho, ho, ho!" laughed the princes,
    "Daniel will be thrown into the lions' den."

The princes wrote the law and took it to the king.
"O king, we wish to honor you," said the sly one.
"We have written a law that anyone who prays to
    any god except you, O king, for thirty days,
    he shall be thrown into the lions' den."
The king was pleased; he asked for wax
    that he might seal the law.
A servant dripped melted wax on the paper.
The king pressed his ring into it; and so
    the law was sealed; it could not be changed.

Messengers were stationed on the city streets
to read the new law to the people.
"Hear ye! Hear ye!" shouted the messengers.
"He who prays to any god
other than the king for thirty days
shall be thrown into the lions' den."

Fathers and mothers stopped to listen;
boys and girls stopped to listen;
Daniel stopped to listen to the reading
of the strange new law.

Several of the princes hurried down the street
    that led to Daniel's house.
They hid where they could see the window
    that he always opened when he prayed.
They saw Daniel come home and go into the house.
Would Daniel open his window and pray as always?
Perhaps he would pray in his closet today.
Maybe he wouldn't pray at all
    until the thirty days were past.
Anxiously the princes watched and waited.
                    And then . . .

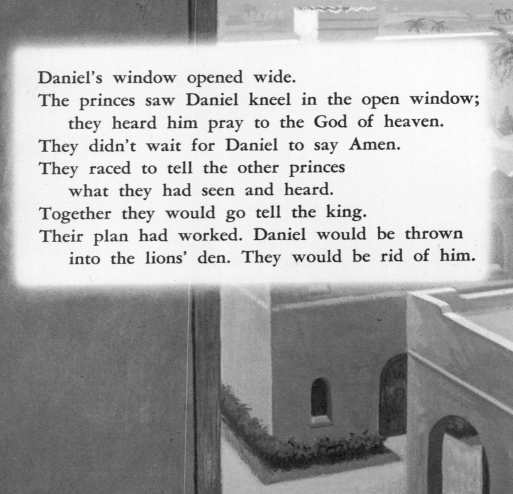

Daniel's window opened wide.
The princes saw Daniel kneel in the open window;
　　they heard him pray to the God of heaven.
They didn't wait for Daniel to say Amen.
They raced to tell the other princes
　　what they had seen and heard.
Together they would go tell the king.
Their plan had worked. Daniel would be thrown
　　into the lions' den. They would be rid of him.

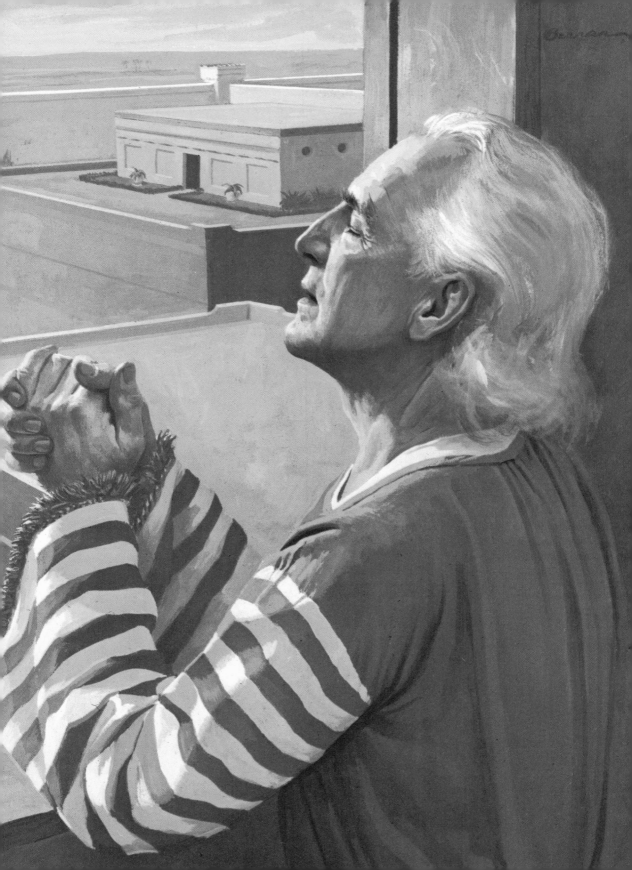

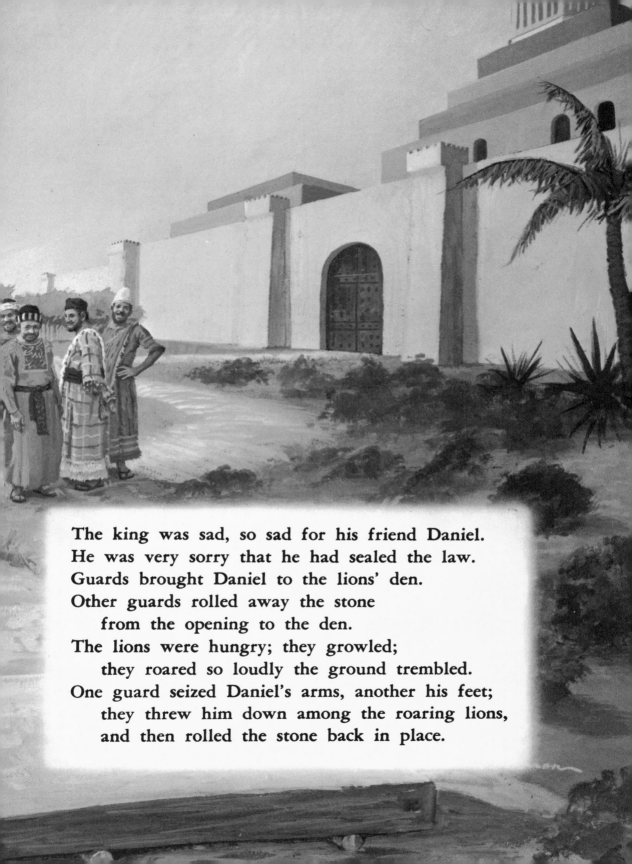

The king was sad, so sad for his friend Daniel.
He was very sorry that he had sealed the law.
Guards brought Daniel to the lions' den.
Other guards rolled away the stone
    from the opening to the den.
The lions were hungry; they growled;
    they roared so loudly the ground trembled.
One guard seized Daniel's arms, another his feet;
    they threw him down among the roaring lions,
    and then rolled the stone back in place.

Suddenly, everything became quiet;
    the lions no longer roared;
    the ground no longer trembled.
The proud princes smiled at one another;
    they were rid of Daniel; they were sure
    they would never see him again.
But the king wept.

Day turned into night:
   the moon came up;
   hundreds and hundreds of stars
   sparkled in the dark night sky.
The king couldn't sleep. He refused to eat;
   he would allow no music to be played.
From time to time he listened toward the window.
Often on other nights the lions roared,
   but tonight the lions were quiet.

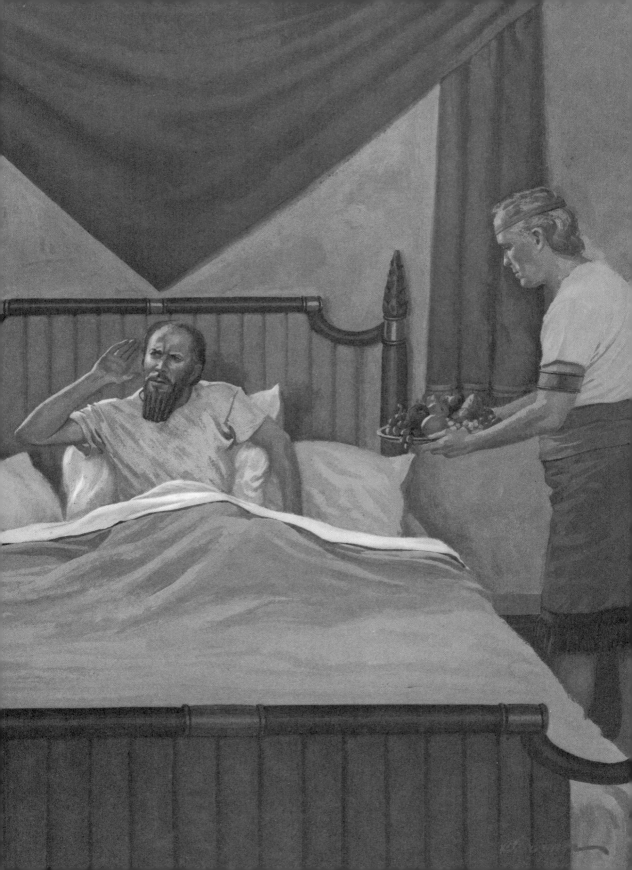

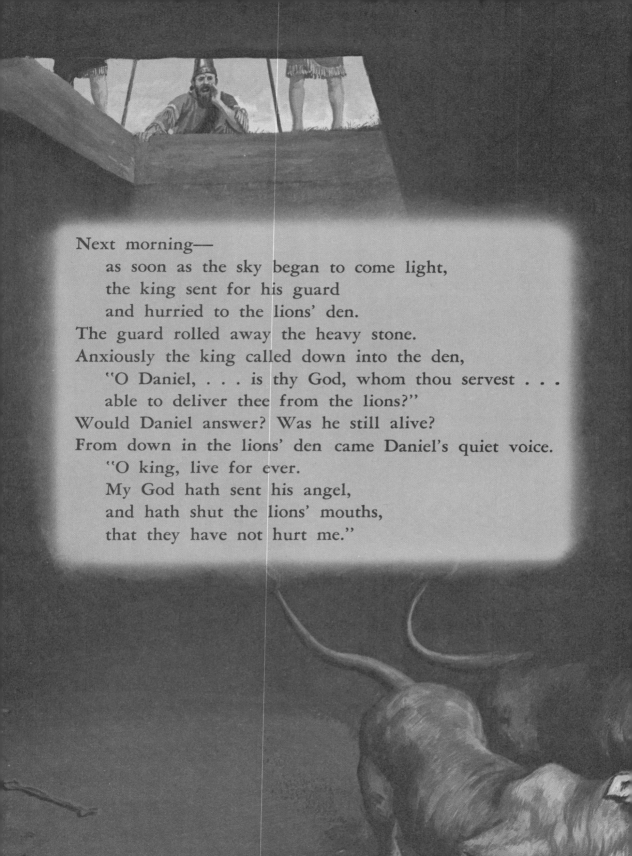

Next morning—
    as soon as the sky began to come light,
    the king sent for his guard
    and hurried to the lions' den.
The guard rolled away the heavy stone.
Anxiously the king called down into the den,
    "O Daniel, . . . is thy God, whom thou servest . . .
    able to deliver thee from the lions?"
Would Daniel answer? Was he still alive?
From down in the lions' den came Daniel's quiet voice.
    "O king, live for ever.
    My God hath sent his angel,
    and hath shut the lions' mouths,
    that they have not hurt me."

Joyously the king ordered the guard
    to take Daniel up out of the lions' den.
The guard let down a rope to Daniel.
Hardly was Daniel out of the den
    when the lions began to roar
    and the ground to tremble.
But there wasn't a tear in Daniel's clothes;
    there wasn't a claw mark on his hands;
    there wasn't a scratch on his face.

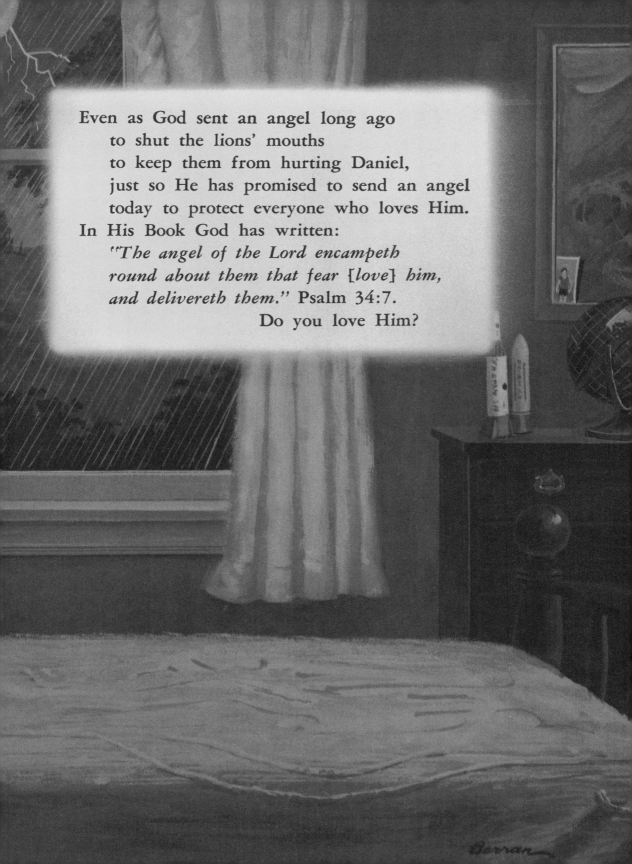

Even as God sent an angel long ago
    to shut the lions' mouths
    to keep them from hurting Daniel,
    just so He has promised to send an angel
    today to protect everyone who loves Him.
In His Book God has written:
    "The angel of the Lord encampeth
    round about them that fear [love] him,
    and delivereth them." Psalm 34:7.
                    Do you love Him?

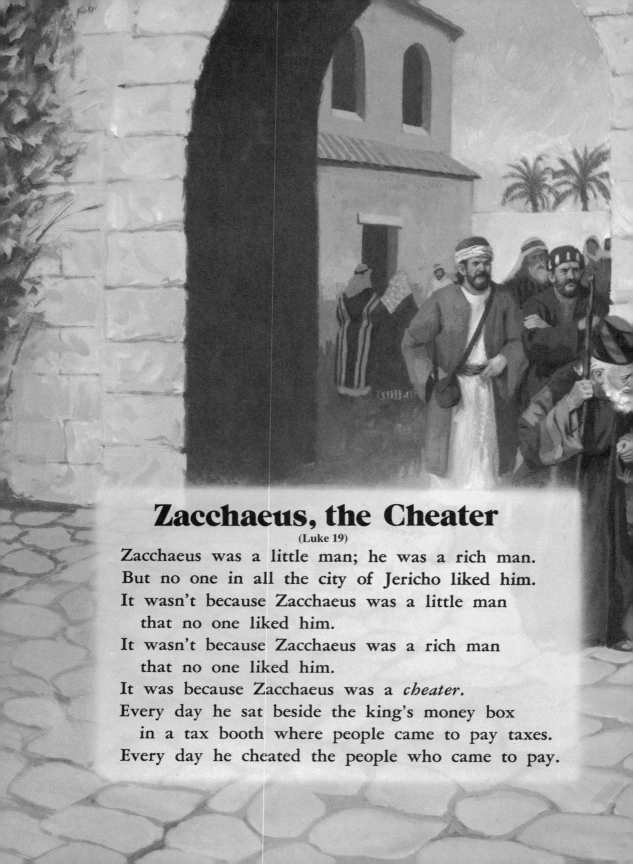

Zacchaeus, the Cheater

(Luke 19)

Zacchaeus was a little man; he was a rich man.
But no one in all the city of Jericho liked him.
It wasn't because Zacchaeus was a little man
    that no one liked him.
It wasn't because Zacchaeus was a rich man
    that no one liked him.
It was because Zacchaeus was a *cheater*.
Every day he sat beside the king's money box
    in a tax booth where people came to pay taxes.
Every day he cheated the people who came to pay.

This is the way Zacchaeus cheated:
If Farmer Philip's tax was one silver coin,
   Zacchaeus charged him more—
   maybe as much as *two* silver coins.
Farmer Philip frowned, but he had to pay.
After Farmer Philip had gone on his way,
   Zacchaeus dropped one of the silver coins
   into the king's money box;
   but the other silver coin
   he slipped into the pocket of his robe.

Camel trains passed through Jericho, carrying
    loads of salt and spice on their humpy backs.
Always the owner of the camel train
    must halt his camels at the tax booth
    and pay tax money on their loads.
And always Zacchaeus charged too much tax money.
Yes, Zacchaeus was a cheater,
    and no one, no one at all, likes a cheater.
But one day something happened
    that changed Zacchaeus' ways.

Down on the riverbank not far from Jericho,
    came John the Baptist to tell about Jesus,
    and to tell about heaven.
Zacchaeus joined the listening crowd at the river.
As he listened, a wish began to grow in his heart.
And the longer he listened, the bigger grew his wish.
Zacchaeus wished he could change his cheating ways.
But how could he change his ways?
"Repent," said John. "Be sorry for your cheating.
    Pay back the money you have wrongly taken."

Zacchaeus hurried away from the river.
He would do as John said:
   he would find Farmer Philip;
   he would find the owner of the camel train,
   and all the other people he had cheated.
He would tell them he was sorry.
He would promise to pay back the tax money
   that he had wrongly taken.
Surely the people would believe him
   when he said, "I'm sorry I cheated you."

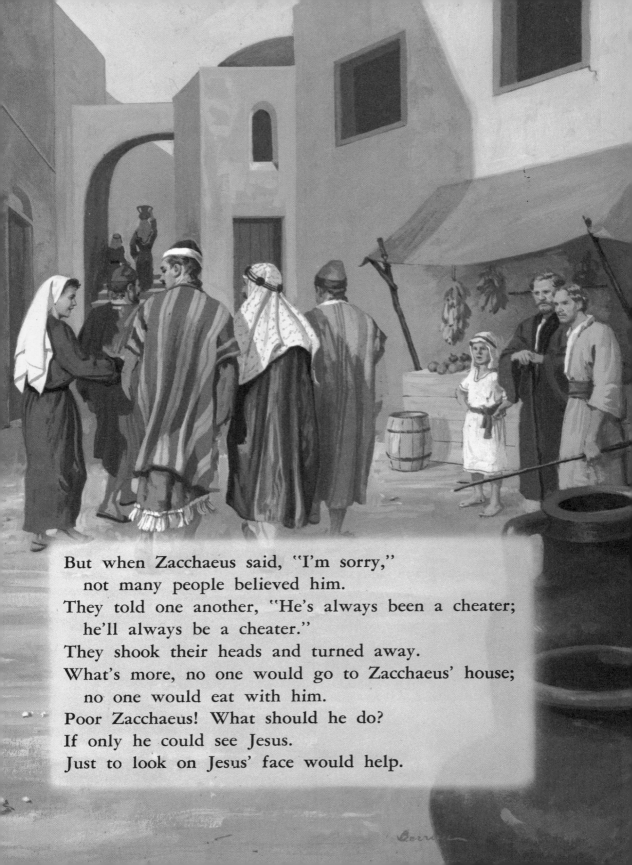

But when Zacchaeus said, "I'm sorry,"
   not many people believed him.
They told one another, "He's always been a cheater;
   he'll always be a cheater."
They shook their heads and turned away.
What's more, no one would go to Zacchaeus' house;
   no one would eat with him.
Poor Zacchaeus! What should he do?
If only he could see Jesus.
Just to look on Jesus' face would help.

And then—one sunshiny morning,
  a messenger came running into the city,
  shouting as he ran, "Ho, everyone!
  Jesus is coming up the road!
  Jesus will pass through Jericho!"
Men and women left their work.
Boys and girls left their play.
They ran to the street where Jesus would pass by.
Zacchaeus didn't even take time to snatch up
  the king's money box; he ran with the crowd.

But when Zacchaeus reached the gate
    where Jesus would enter Jericho,
    the narrow street was jammed with people.
He was too short to see over their heads
    and no one would make room for him.
Zacchaeus ran here, he ran there,
    trying to find a place where he could see.
He *must* see Jesus. He *had* to see Jesus.
But how could he? And then—
    Zacchaeus remembered something.

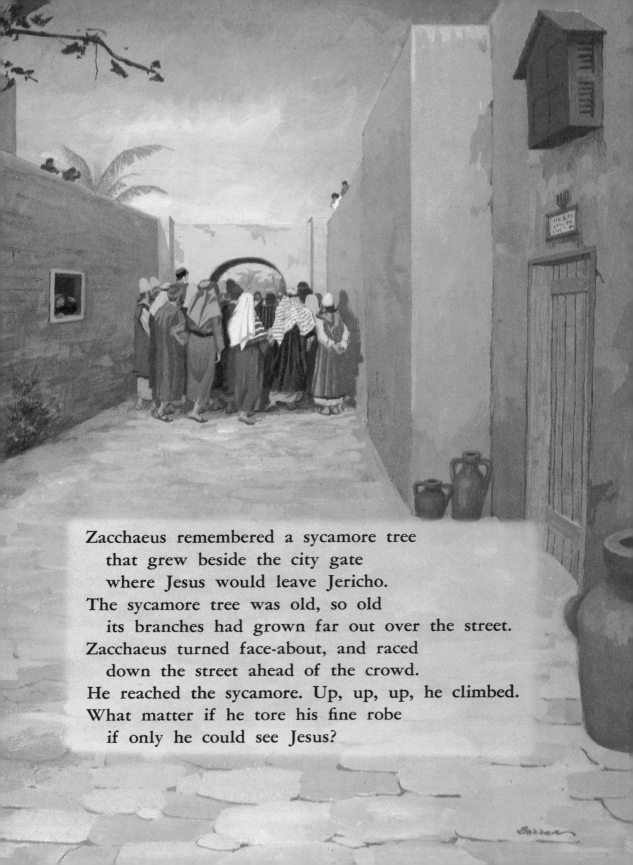

Zacchaeus remembered a sycamore tree
    that grew beside the city gate
    where Jesus would leave Jericho.
The sycamore tree was old, so old
    its branches had grown far out over the street.
Zacchaeus turned face-about, and raced
    down the street ahead of the crowd.
He reached the sycamore. Up, up, up, he climbed.
What matter if he tore his fine robe
    if only he could see Jesus?

Zacchaeus climbed out on a branch of the sycamore.
He could see the throng far up the street.
People were shouting; some waved palm branches.
Zacchaeus shaded his eyes to see better.
The man dressed in the white robe,
    around whom all the crowd pressed—
    that man must be Jesus.
And those men trying to make room for Him to walk,
    they must be Jesus' disciples.
Slowly the crowd came nearer and nearer.

Closer—closer—closer came the crowd
    toward the sycamore tree beside the gate.
Now Zacchaeus could see Jesus' face.
Never had he seen a face so kind.
If only he could talk to Jesus—
    tell Him he was sorry he had cheated;
    tell Him he would pay back all of
    the tax money he had falsely taken.
Would Jesus believe him? Or like those others,
    would Jesus shake His head and turn away?

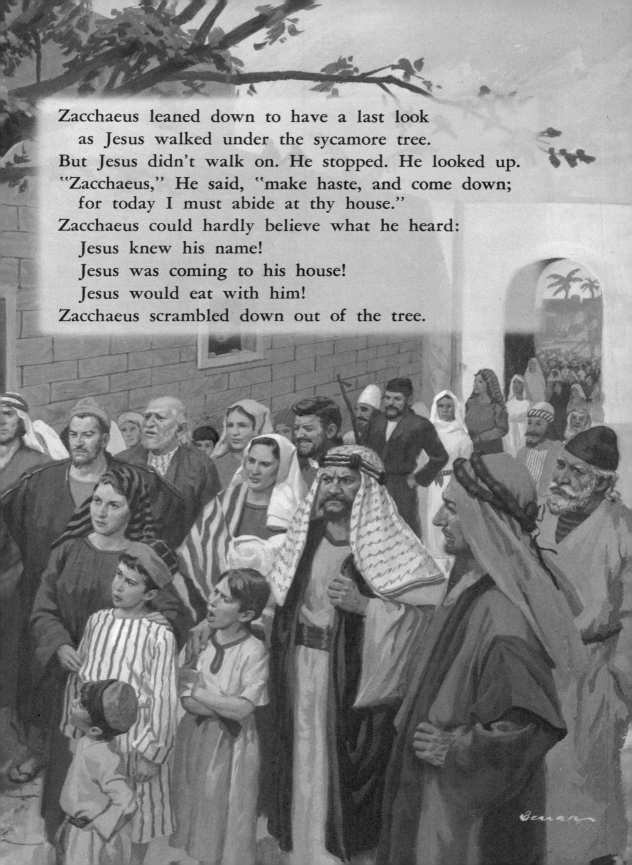

Zacchaeus leaned down to have a last look
   as Jesus walked under the sycamore tree.
But Jesus didn't walk on. He stopped. He looked up.
"Zacchaeus," He said, "make haste, and come down;
   for today I must abide at thy house."
Zacchaeus could hardly believe what he heard:
   Jesus knew his name!
   Jesus was coming to his house!
   Jesus would eat with him!
Zacchaeus scrambled down out of the tree.

At the foot of the sycamore tree,
Zacchaeus stood before Jesus
and made a promise—no,
he made *two* promises.

"Lord," he said, "the half of all that I own
    I am giving to the poor, and
    if I have taken anything falsely,
    I am paying it back four times."
Jesus held out His hand to Zacchaeus.
JESUS BELIEVED HIM!

Jesus believes *me*,
When beside my bed I pray,
"I'm sorry, Jesus,
That I cheated in a game today."

He holds out His hand,
As He did beneath the sycamore.
"I believe you, child.
Tomorrow play—but cheat no more."

Jabel, the Shepherd

(Matthew 18, Luke 15)

Jabel, the shepherd, lived in a little stone hut
　　on a rocky mountainside in Judea.
Ten steps and a jump from the little stone hut
　　Jabel had built his sheepfold,
　　　　laying stone upon stone upon stone.
Jabel owned one hundred sheep.
There were rams with curled horns
　　and ewes with small lambs.
All of the sheep—rams, ewes, and lambs—
　　had thick woolly coats and long fatty tails.

Jabel's sheep obeyed him. When Jabel called
  "Ta-a-a-a, ho-o-o! {Come to me},"
  his one hundred sheep came running,
  their hoofs click-click-clacking
  on the stony ground of the mountain.

When Jabel made the sound of a dog howling,
  "O-o-o-h! O-o-o-h! {Press together},"
  the sheep huddled in a tight little group.

And when Jabel said "La-a-a, la-a-a! {Lie down},"
  all the one hundred sheep lay down.

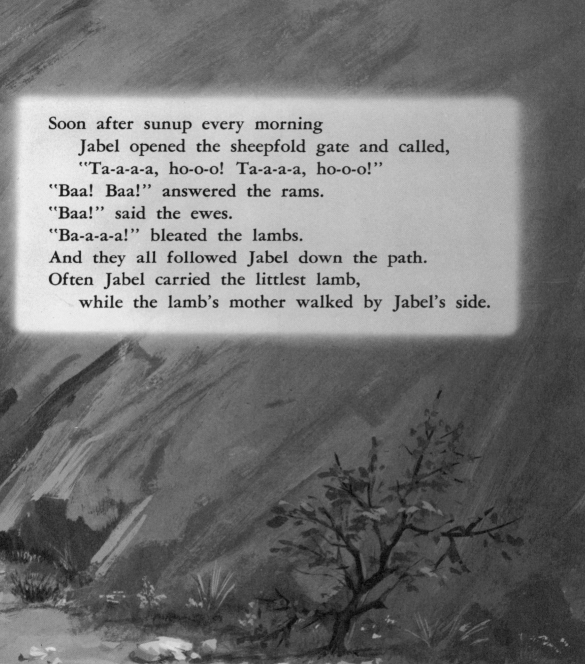

Soon after sunup every morning
 Jabel opened the sheepfold gate and called,
  "Ta-a-a-a, ho-o-o! Ta-a-a-a, ho-o-o!"
"Baa! Baa!" answered the rams.
"Baa!" said the ewes.
"Ba-a-a-a!" bleated the lambs.
And they all followed Jabel down the path.
Often Jabel carried the littlest lamb,
 while the lamb's mother walked by Jabel's side.

Jabel led his one hundred sheep
    to a green grassy place where they could feed.
But at the edge of the green grassy place
    he called, "La-a-a, la-a-a! La-a-a, la-a-a!"
And although the sheep were hungry, they lay down.
Jabel carefully searched the green grassy place
    for poisonous weeds and poisonous snakes.
The weeds he pulled up; and when he hit the ground
    with his staff, the snakes wiggled away.
Now that the green grassy place was safe for sheep,
    Jabel called, "Ta-a-a-a, ho-o-o! Come eat!"

While the rams and the ewes nibbled grass,
   the lambs played follow-the-leader.
Around a bush here, and another one there,
   jumping over a not-too-big rock,
   the lambs raced one after the other.
When a lamb became hungry,
   he didn't nibble grass,
   he got milk from his mother.
And all the while Jabel stood by,
   keeping watch over his one hundred sheep.

In the afternoon Jabel called "Ta-a-a-a, ho-o-o!"
    And led his sheep away from the green grassy place.
A long way they must now go to find water.
One drink a day was all the sheep needed,
    but one drink they must have.
The path was stony; the bushes, thorny;
    the caves along the way, dark and deep
    where Jabel led his one hundred sheep.
Out of a cave came a hungry wolf,
    sneaking, sneaking along behind the sheep.

When the path led into a valley,
the wolf, with a snarl and a leap,
rushed at the flock of one hundred sheep.
The wolf's plan was to scatter the sheep,
then chase a ewe or a lamb
back up the valley toward his wolf cave,
far away from the shepherd
and the shepherd's stout staff.

In a flash Jabel leaped to a rock, calling,
 "O-o-o-h! O-o-o-h! O-o-o-h!"
And though the sheep were scared and wanted to run,
 they obeyed Jabel's call.
Together they pressed, tighter, tighter, tighter,
 so tight the wolf could not scatter them.
Then Jabel jumped down from the rock,
 and with his long staff
 he whacked and he thwacked the robber wolf,
 and drove him away from the sheep.

After the battle with the wolf,
    Jabel called a gentle "Ta-a-a-a, ho-o-o!"
    and led his sheep on down the path.
Soon they came to a splashing, dashing stream.
Now sheep cannot drink from a splashing,
    dashing stream, but Jabel knew what to do.
He told his sheep "La-a-a, la-a-a."
Then he dammed up the splashing, dashing stream
    to make a quiet pool where they could drink.
But one sheep disobeyed. Behind Jabel's back
    one sheep slipped away up over the mountain.

When the sheep had finished drinking
  at the quiet pool, Jabel led them home,
  carrying by turn the tired lambs.
At the sheepfold gate he counted his sheep
  as they entered one at a time.
"One, two, three"—he stooped to put cedar gum
  on a wound made by the wolf's fangs.
"Four, five, six"—he poured oil on a tired ewe's head.
On and on and on he counted to the last sheep.
But the count did not come out right—
                    ONE SHEEP WAS MISSING!

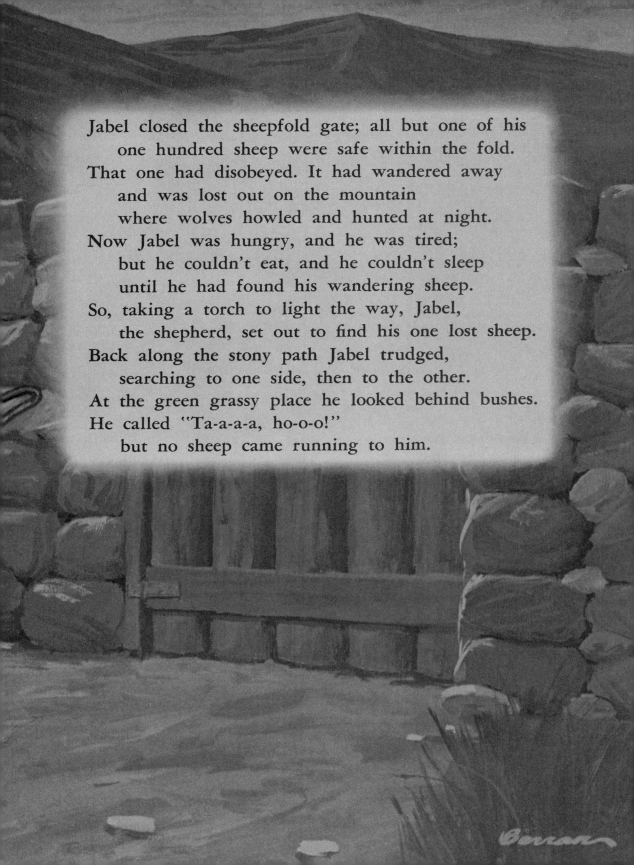

Jabel closed the sheepfold gate; all but one of his
    one hundred sheep were safe within the fold.
That one had disobeyed. It had wandered away
    and was lost out on the mountain
    where wolves howled and hunted at night.
Now Jabel was hungry, and he was tired;
    but he couldn't eat, and he couldn't sleep
    until he had found his wandering sheep.
So, taking a torch to light the way, Jabel,
    the shepherd, set out to find his one lost sheep.
Back along the stony path Jabel trudged,
    searching to one side, then to the other.
At the green grassy place he looked behind bushes.
He called "Ta-a-a-a, ho-o-o!"
    but no sheep came running to him.

Past the deep dark caves where the wolf lived,
　　on to the splashing, dashing stream, walked Jabel.
Beside the quiet pool he stopped and called again,
　　"Ta-a-a-a, ho-o-o! Ta-a-a-a, ho-o-o!"
Listen! Did he hear an answer?
"Baa!" came faintly from over the mountain. "Baa!"
Jabel climbed the mountain, and there,
　　down a steep bank, he found his lost sheep
　　trapped in a thorny thicket.
With his staff Jabel rescued the frightened sheep.
Then placing it across his shoulder,
　　he carried it the long way home.

Jabel sang as he closed the sheepfold gate,
　　for safe inside were his one hundred sheep.

Jesus says, "I am the good shepherd."
"My sheep hear my voice . . . and . . . follow me."
Jesus' sheep are all the people of the world,
    brown or black, red, yellow, or white.
The children are His lambs.
Jesus cares for His sheep and lambs as did Jabel.
He calls, "Come unto Me:
        I will give you food;
        I will give you water;
        I will keep you safe."